Learning Train
6412 Maple Ave.
Westminster, CA 92683
www.learningtrainpub.com
ISBN: 978-1-4206-5900-9

Reprinted, 2008
Made in U.S.A.

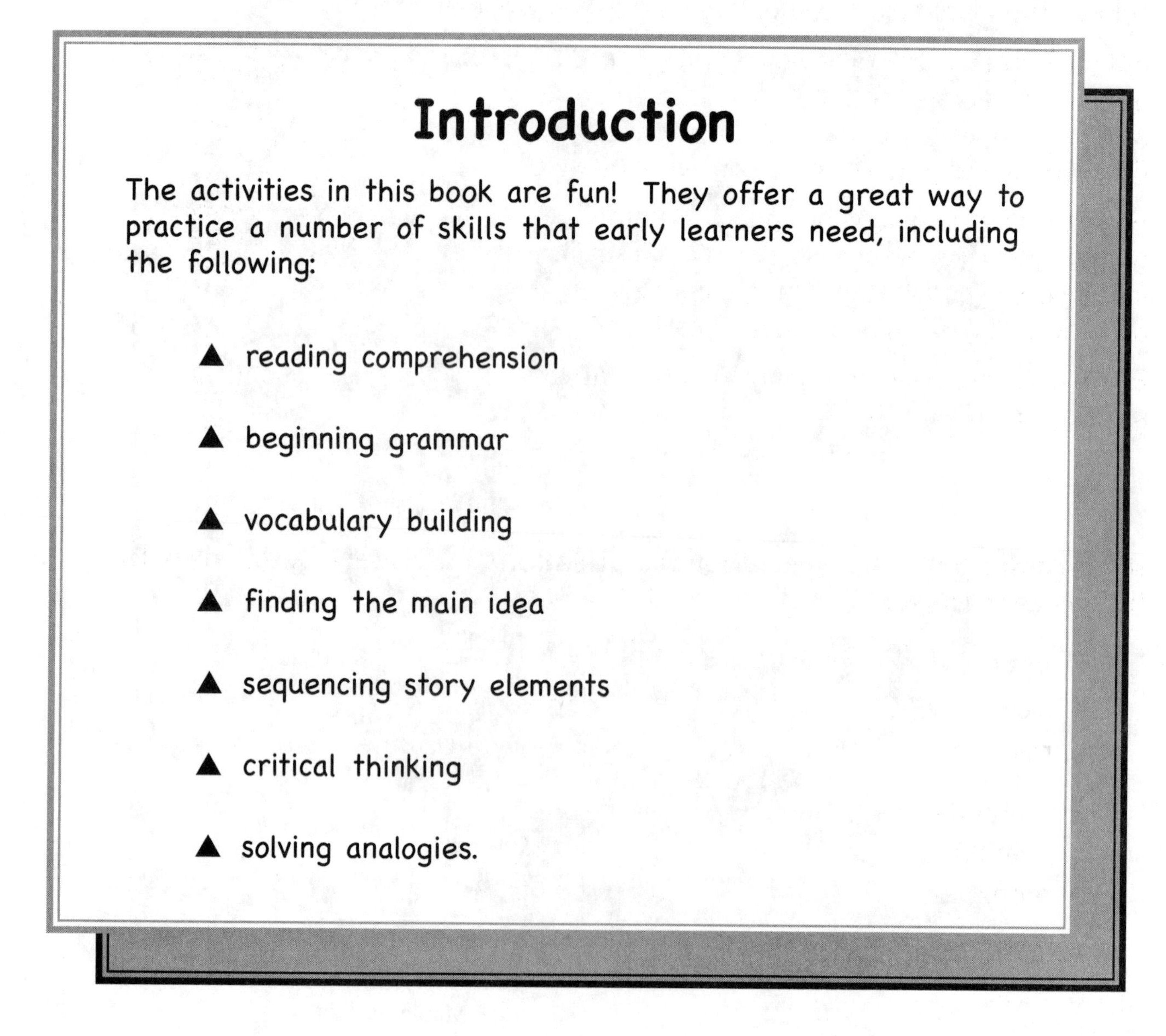

Introduction

The activities in this book are fun! They offer a great way to practice a number of skills that early learners need, including the following:

- ▲ reading comprehension
- ▲ beginning grammar
- ▲ vocabulary building
- ▲ finding the main idea
- ▲ sequencing story elements
- ▲ critical thinking
- ▲ solving analogies.

Foods with Color

Red berries. Orange carrots. Green peppers. Fruits and vegetables come in many colors. The more colors you eat, the better you will feel!

Eat your greens. Broccoli, spinach, and dark green lettuce are good for you. You can make a salad or a tasty stir-fry dish. Eat your blues, too. Blueberries and grapes will keep your body well.

Red foods like tomatoes are good. So are orange foods like oranges and carrots. Don't forget yellow foods! Bananas are not only for monkeys. They will keep you healthy, too.

Every day, your plate can be full of color. Try to see how many colors you can eat at every meal.

After reading the story, answer the questions. Circle the letter next to the correct answer.

1. If you eat many colors, you will feel . . .

a. sick.
b. rainbows.
c. healthy.
d. blue.

2. You can make a salad out of . . .

a. spinach.
b. monkeys.
c. crayons.
d. yellow.

3. Grapes will keep your body . . .

a. full.
b. sick.
c. blue.
d. well.

4. Every day, your plate should be full of . . .

a. color.
b. monkeys.
c. dessert.
d. cake.

Volcanoes

Where does the word <u>*volcano*</u> come from? It comes from the Roman god of fire. His name was Vulcan.

A volcano is a mountain that blows its top! Hot lava pushes through the mountain. Then, it flows down the side.

Some volcanoes are millions of years old. Some sleep. Others are active. It is <u>hard</u> to tell when a volcano will blow.

Many volcanoes have snow. If they blow their tops, hot lava melts the snow. It burns up trees and plants, too, just like a fire.

After reading the story, answer the questions. Circle the letter next to the correct answer.

1. The word *volcano* comes from the Roman god of . . .
   - a. heat.
   - b. burn.
   - c. fire.
   - d. sun.
2. What pushes through a mountain to make a volcano?
   - a. ice
   - b. fire
   - c. snow
   - d. lava
3. In this story, the word *hard* means . . .
   - a. difficult.
   - b. solid.
   - c. wood.
   - d. mean.
4. Who is Vulcan?
   - a. a volcano
   - b. a tree
   - c. a mountain
   - d. a Roman god

Millipedes

The millipede is small but strong. It can have between 80 and 400 legs!

Millipedes walk slowly. Still, they can dig long tunnels. They wave their legs and push underground head first.

These creatures eat dead leaves and plants. They wet the food and scrape at it with their jaws.

When scared, the millipede curls into a ball. Its back is hard, like armor. This protects its legs. Millipedes also have poison. It burns ants, but it doesn't hurt people.

Never step on a millipede. It has places to go and tunnels to dig!

After reading the story, answer the questions. Circle the letter next to the correct answer.

1. How many legs can a millipede have?

a. 40
b. 90
c. 600
d. 10

2. How do millipedes dig tunnels?

a. with a shovel
b. with their teeth
c. with their legs and heads
d. with a spoon

3. In this story, *scrape* means . . .

a. to gnaw at something.
b. to skin your knee.
c. to carve a branch.
d. to get into trouble.

4. Why should you never step on a millipede?

a. because it burns ants
b. because it has lots of legs
c. because it has tunnels to dig
d. because it curls into a ball

The Apple Thief

Mom loved apples. She liked to put them in oatmeal. She liked to eat them right off the tree. She liked to bake pies with them.

Mom and Maria lived on a farm. They had horses and cows. They had a lot of land. One day, she planted an apple tree. "Now, we can have fresh apples," she told Maria.

First, the tree had flowers. Then it had little green apples. Finally, the apples were red and ripe. "Tomorrow, we will pick them," said Mom.

But the next morning, all the apples were gone. "Did you pick the apples?" Mom asked Maria.

"No," said Maria.

"Then where are they?"

They looked and looked. Then, they saw their black pony. She was lying down. Her tummy was swollen. She looked very full. "Look who ate the apples!" said Mom.

After reading the story, answer the questions. Circle the letter next to the correct answer.

1. Why is the pony's tummy swollen?

a. She has eaten Maria.
b. She has eaten a tree.
c. She has eaten flowers.
d. She has eaten the apples.

2. Where do Mom and Maria live?

a. in an apple tree
b. in the horse stall
c. in a city
d. on a farm

3. What is **true** about this story?

a. Mom does not have a horse.
b. The pony eats all the apples.
c. Maria eats all the apples.
d. The pony is white.

4. In this story, *lying* means . . .

a. resting.
b. telling a lie.
c. being dishonest.
d. sitting on a chair.

Planet Cat

John stepped out of the spaceship, and Cat Leader shook his hand. "Nice to meet you," she said. "Welcome to Planet Cat."

John looked around. A cat put down a bowl of milk. A boy licked it with his tongue. Another cat brushed a girl's long ponytail. "What is going on here?" John cried.

Cat Leader purred. "Here, we keep boys and girls as pets."

Then John saw a cat toss a ball of yarn. A girl chased it. He saw another cat put a bell around a boy's arm. "This is so you cannot catch birds," said the cat.

John got back into his spaceship. He headed home to Earth. His cat greeted him at the front door. He gave her a bowl of milk and brushed her fur. "I'm glad you are my pet," he said.

After reading the story, answer the questions. Circle the letter next to the correct answer.

1. On Planet Cat, boys and girls are . . .

a. pets. c. birds.
b. cats. d. aliens.

2. On this planet, cats . . .

a. chase balls of yarn. c. catch birds.
b. lick milk with their tongues. d. brush people's hair.

3. John lives on Planet . . .

a. Cat. c. Bird.
b. Earth. d. Space.

4. What is **not true** about this story?

a. Cats treat girls and boys like pets.
b. John has a pet cat.
c. The cats are mean to people.
d. John lands on Planet Cat.

Emily's Rocket

Emily wanted to build a rocket. "I will go to Mars," she said. "I will go to Pluto. I will even visit the moon."

Scotty laughed. "You don't know how to build a rocket!"

"I'll show you," said Emily. She found some wood and some nails. She found a hammer. She found an old pie tin and some bike pedals. She began to work.

At last, Emily was done. "Turn these bike pedals," she told Scotty. She climbed into the rocket.

He laughed again. "This will never work," he said. But he turned the pedals.

Suddenly, Emily was gone! The rocket shot straight up into the air. It landed on Mars, and Emily stepped out. "I showed you!" she called down to Scotty on Earth.

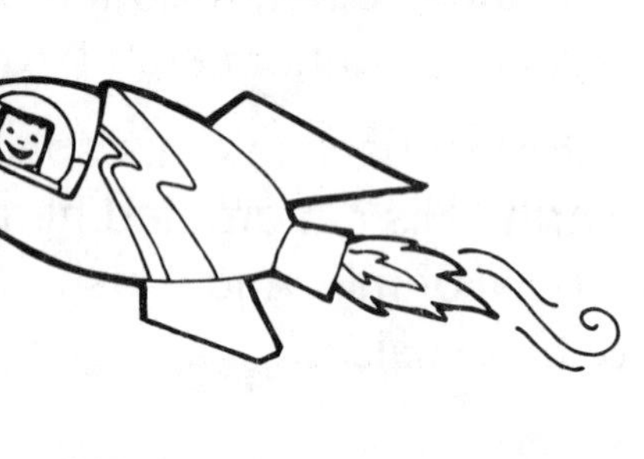

But he was gone. He'd made a rocket of his own, and he was waiting for Emily on Pluto.

After reading the story, answer the questions. Circle the letter next to the correct answer.

1. Why does Scotty laugh at Emily?

a. He thinks she can build a rocket.

b. He thinks her plan is silly.

c. He wants to eat pie.

d. He wants to ride his bike.

2. Emily makes her rocket out of . . .

a. flowers.

b. bikes.

c. wood, tin, and bike pedals.

d. wood, pie, and bike tires.

3. What happens when Scotty turns the pedals?

a. The rocket crashes.

b. Nothing.

c. The rocket goes to Pluto.

d. The rocket shoots into the air.

4. What is **true** about this story?

a. Emily laughs at Scotty.

b. Emily can not use a hammer.

c. Emily is creative.

d. Scott stops Emily from going.

Glenda Goldfish

Glenda was a goldfish. She lived in a bowl on Nick's desk. She had fresh water. She had a little castle. But she was bored. "I want to swim in the ocean," Glenda said. "I want to see the world."

One night it got windy. Nick forgot to close his window. The wind was so strong that it picked Glenda up out of her bowl. The rain washed her into the gutter. She floated along until she came to the ocean!

"At last!" said Glenda. "I can see the world!"

But she was a small fish, and the world was very big. A whale tried to eat her. She missed her castle. "I wish I could go back to my bowl," Glenda said. She swam out of the ocean and back up the gutter. She waited in a puddle outside Nick's house. When he saw her, he smiled. "You came back!" he cried and put her back in her bowl.

After reading the story, answer the questions. Circle the letter next to the correct answer.

1. Where does Glenda live?
   - a. in the gutter
   - b. in a puddle
   - c. in a desk
   - d. in a bowl

2. Why does Glenda want to see the world?
   - a. She is bored.
   - b. She does not like Nick.
   - c. She is a whale.
   - d. She does not have fresh water.

3. In this story, *washed* means
   - a. soap and water.
   - b. pushed.
   - c. laundry.
   - d. castle.

4. Where does Nick find Glenda?
   - a. in a castle
   - b. in a gutter
   - c. in a puddle
   - d. in the ocean

When a Rat Can Be a Fish

Ms. Jo's class was getting a pet. It would be the class pet. Would the pet be a fish? Would the pet be a rat? "Fish swim in schools," said Ray. "The class pet should be a fish. Then, it can be in a school."

Liz said, "You cannot hold a fish. You can hold a rat. I want a pet I can hold. The class should have a rat. It should have a rat as a pet."

Ms. Jo said, "Our class is a democracy. We will vote. We are a direct democracy. This means that everyone gets one vote. Each vote counts the same. You can vote directly for a fish. You can vote directly for a rat. We will count up the votes. The animal with the most votes will win. The animal with the least votes will lose."

The class voted. They counted the votes. What was the class pet going to be? The rat had the most votes. The fish had the least votes. Ray said, "Our class is a direct democracy. We each got one vote. Each vote counted the same. It was a fair vote. The rat wins. The fish loses. We will get a rat. That is the animal most of the class wants. It is only fair."

Liz looked at Ray. She said, "I have an idea. I think the class will like this idea. We can name the rat. We can name it 'Fish.' Then we will have a Fish. Our Fish will be a rat. Our Fish will be in a school." The class began to laugh. They thought it was funny. Then, they took a vote. Everyone got one vote. Each vote counted the same. What did the class want? They all wanted a rat named Fish!

When a Rat Can Be a Fish

After reading the story, answer the questions.
Fill in the circle next to the correct answer.

1. This story is mainly about

ⓐ Liz and Ray.
ⓑ picking a class pet.
ⓒ how fish swim in schools.
ⓓ counting in Ms. Jo's class.

2. How many times did the class vote?

ⓐ 1
ⓑ 2
ⓒ 3
ⓓ 4

3. Think about how the word *win* relates to *most*. What words relate in the same way?

win : most

ⓐ lose : least
ⓑ vote : count
ⓒ fish : school
ⓓ class : democracy

4. In a direct democracy,

ⓐ everyone counts votes.
ⓑ everyone votes the same.
ⓒ everyone gets the most votes.
ⓓ everyone gets one vote that counts the same.

5. From the vote, you can tell that

ⓐ most of the class wanted a fish.
ⓑ all of the class wanted a pet they could hold.
ⓒ most of the class wanted a pet they could hold.
ⓓ all of the class wanted a fish they could hold.

Spiders

A spider has eight legs. It has eight eyes. Most spiders help us. Only a few spiders can hurt us. Many spiders protect plants. How do spiders protect plants? Spiders eat insects. They eat insects that eat plants.

Spiders can spin silk. They can spin fat silk. They can spin thin silk. They can spin sticky silk. They can spin slippery silk, too. All spiders can spin silk, but only some spiders build webs. Web-building spiders wait. They wait to trap insects in their webs. Other spiders hunt. They hunt for crawling insects.

Some spiders are orb weavers. Orb weavers build webs shaped like an orb. An orb is like a circle. When an insect hits the web, the spider feels the web vibrating. When something is vibrating, it is moving back and forth. The spider rushes to the insect. It wraps it up. It wraps it up with sticky silk. Then, it bites it. This way the spider does not get hurt. This way the spider can wait to eat.

One spider is a "net-thrower." The spider makes a net with its silk. Then it hangs upside down. It holds its net. It waits for an insect to crawl by. When an insect crawls by, the spider throws its net. It throws its net over the crawling insect!

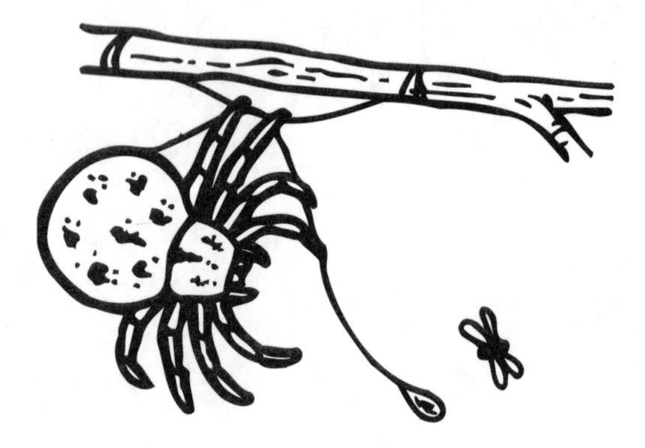

One spider spins a ball of sticky silk. It fastens the sticky ball to a line. The line is made of strong silk. Then, the spider tricks male moths. The spider makes the smell of the female moth. Male moths come to find the female moth. When a male moth comes, the spider hits it with the sticky ball of silk! The moth gets stuck. The spider then pulls in its line. The spider gets the stuck moth!

Spiders

After reading the story, answer the questions.
Fill in the circle next to the correct answer.

1. What does an orb weaver's web look like?

ⓐ a net
ⓑ a ball
ⓒ a line
ⓓ a circle

2. When something is vibrating, it

ⓐ protects plants.
ⓑ hangs upside down.
ⓒ moves back and forth.
ⓓ smells like a female moth.

3. This story is mainly about

ⓐ webs.
ⓑ silk.
ⓒ insects.
ⓓ spiders.

4. Which statement is true?

ⓐ All spiders can spin silk.
ⓑ All spiders can build webs.
ⓒ Some spiders have eight legs.
ⓓ Some spiders have eight eyes.

5. Think about how the word **boy** relates to **girl**. Which words relate in the same way?

boy : girl

ⓐ web : net
ⓑ male : female
ⓒ insect : spider
ⓓ plant : protect

Glacier: Ice on the Move

A man was walking. It was 1933. He saw a sheep. The man looked again. Could he believe his eyes? Yes, it was a sheep. It was a mountain sheep. It was a kind of sheep that was not alive anymore! It was extinct. When something is extinct, it is no longer alive.

The mountain sheep did not move. The man went close. Still, the sheep did not move. The man went closer. He touched the sheep. The sheep was not alive. It was frozen. Long ago, the sheep had fallen into a crack. The crack was in a glacier. Over time, the glacier had moved. Over time, ice at the glacier's end had melted. After many years, the sheep was free of ice.

What is a glacier? A glacier is snow and ice. It snows. Fresh snow falls on the old snow. More and more snow falls. Every year, more snow falls. The pile of snow gets big. All the snow is heavy. It presses on the old bottom snow. The snow on the bottom melts. It turns to ice.

The ice at the bottom begins to move. It spreads out. It goes downhill. When the snow pile begins to move, it is called a glacier. The glacier moves at different speeds. The bottom moves faster. The bottom ice moves faster. It moves faster than the snow and ice at the top. The glacier cracks. It cracks as its top and bottom move at different speeds.

Glaciers that spread out are called ice sheets. The ice sheet near the South Pole is thick. It is more than 2 miles (3 kilometers) thick! Glaciers that go downhill are called valley glaciers. They flow between mountains. Most valley glaciers flow about 650 feet (200 meters) a year.

Glacier: Ice on the Move

After reading the story, answer the questions.
Fill in the circle next to the correct answer.

1. A glacier that flows between mountains is called

ⓐ a crack.
ⓑ an ice sheet.
ⓒ a fresh glacier.
ⓓ a valley glacier.

2. Why do cracks form in glaciers?

ⓐ ice at the glacier's end melts
ⓑ fresh snow presses on the old bottom snow
ⓒ bottom ice flows faster than top snow and ice
ⓓ top snow and ice flows faster than bottom ice

3. This story is mainly about

ⓐ glaciers.
ⓑ ice sheets.
ⓒ snow and ice.
ⓓ a frozen sheep.

4. When something is extinct,

ⓐ it is frozen.
ⓑ it is a sheep.
ⓒ it flows downhill.
ⓓ it is no longer alive.

5. Think about how the word **fresh** relates to **old**. Which words relate in the same way?

fresh : old

ⓐ speed : move
ⓑ ice : spread
ⓒ top : bottom
ⓓ glacier : snow

Money Questions

Can money be as heavy as stone? Can money be as light as a feather? The answer is yes. Money can be as heavy as stone. Money can be as light as a feather.

Long ago, there was no money. People would not pay with money. They would barter. When you barter, you trade. Maybe you wanted a cow. You did not pay money for the cow. You bartered for it. You traded something for it. You might trade cloth. You might trade food.

Money made buying easier. It made selling easier. Say you wanted a cow. You did not have to barter for it. You did not have to have something the seller wanted. You could just pay for it. You could just use money. The cow seller could take money from anyone. Then, he or she could spend the money. The seller could use the money to pay for anything he or she wanted to buy. He or she could buy cloth. He or she could buy food.

Today, our money is not as heavy as stone. But long ago, some money was! The Yap people live on an island. The island is in the South Pacific. The people of Yap used stone discs as money. The discs were round. A hole went through the middle. Some of the discs were big. The biggest one was 12 feet (4 meters) across!

Today, our money is not as light as a feather. But long ago, some money was! Santa Cruz is an island in the Pacific. The people on the island used feathers. Tiny red feathers were used as money. The feathers were glued on flat fibers. The fibers were rolled up. They were made into coils. Some of the coils were 30 feet (10 meters) long!

Money Questions

After reading the story, answer the questions.
Fill in the circle next to the correct answer.

1. What is *not* true about old Yap money?
   - (a) It was round.
   - (b) It was made of stone.
   - (c) It had feathers glued on it.
   - (d) It had a hole in the middle of it.

2. This story is mainly about
   - (a) money.
   - (b) bartering.
   - (c) selling cows.
   - (d) stones and feathers.

3. Why did money make it easier to buy a cow?
   - (a) You could trade cloth for a cow.
   - (b) You could barter with the seller.
   - (c) You did not have to have food to barter.
   - (d) You did not have to have something the seller wanted.

4. Think about how the word *buy* relates to *sell*. What words relate in the same way?

   buy : sell

   - (a) heavy : light
   - (b) barter : trade
   - (c) stone : feather
   - (d) island : Pacific

5. When you coil a rope you
   - (a) glue it.
   - (b) roll it up.
   - (c) put a hole in it.
   - (d) barter or trade it.

Something Wrong

We go to museums. We go to look. We look at things. An aquarium is a museum. It is a museum with fish. Aquariums have lots of tanks. The tanks are filled with fish. The fish come from all over. One big aquarium had lots of tanks. It had lots of fish. The fish were from all over. But something was wrong. Something was wrong in the aquarium.

In the day, nothing was wrong. All the fish were fine. The aquarium closed at night. No one was there. No one could get in. In the morning, it was not fine. Fish were missing. Something was going on at night. Something wrong was going on. People in the aquarium set up a camera. The camera would take pictures. It would take pictures at night. The pictures would show what was going on.

What was wrong? What did the pictures show? They showed an octopus! They showed an octopus climbing. It was climbing out of its tank. It was going into other tanks. It was eating fish in other tanks. When it was full, it would go back. It would go back to its own tank. In the morning, the octopus was always in its own tank.

How was the octopus climbing? How was it getting out of its tank? It was using its arms. An octopus has eight arms. The arms have suckers. The suckers are round. The suckers are used to grab things. They are used to taste things. They are used to feel things.

The arms are flexible. When something is flexible, it can bend. It can move easily. Why are octopus arms so flexible? Why do they bend so easily? They have no bones. In fact, an octopus does not have any bones at all!

Something Wrong

**After reading the story, answer the questions.
Fill in the circle next to the correct answer.**

1. This story is mainly about

ⓐ a museum and what you see.
ⓑ suckers and what they can do.
ⓒ an aquarium and what was in it.
ⓓ an octopus and what it was doing.

2. Why did people in the museum set up a camera?

ⓐ They wanted to look at pictures.
ⓑ They wanted to see what was going on at night.
ⓒ They wanted to see an octopus with eight arms.
ⓓ They wanted to see what was going on in the day.

3. When something is flexible,

ⓐ it can climb.
ⓑ it is in a museum.
ⓒ it has eight arms.
ⓓ it can bend easily.

4. Think about how the word **fish** relates to **aquarium**. Which words relate in the same way?

fish : aquarium

ⓐ house : tank
ⓑ slide : park
ⓒ animals : zoo
ⓓ museum : look

5. What does an octopus uses its suckers on its arms for?

ⓐ to bend, grab, and feel
ⓑ to eat, grab, and taste
ⓒ to grab, taste, and feel
ⓓ to climb, eat, and taste

A Game Played Around the World

Over 2,000 years ago, a game was played. It was played in China. It was played in Japan. It was played in Greece. It was played in Italy. The games were very much alike. They all had balls. The balls were kicked or carried. It was kicked or carried through a goal. A game we play today comes from these old games. It is the game of soccer.

Long ago, what did people use for a ball? They used animal skins. The animal skins were stuffed. They used pigs' bladders, too. A bladder is like a bag. It can hold liquid. But the people would not fill the pig's bladder with liquid. They would fill it with air.

In 1863, some people met. They met in England. They wanted to set up rules. The rules would be for soccer. Why did they want rules? Before, every team and school had its own rules. Some teams said players could hold the ball. Some teams said players could trip each other. The people wanted the rules to be the same in all soccer games.

Today, soccer is played all around the world. When two teams play, it is a fair game. When something is fair, it is the same. Why is it fair? The rules are the same. They are the same for both teams. In most places, soccer is called football. Long ago, soccer in the United States was known as "association football." This took too long to write. It took too long to say. People shortened it to "assoc." This led to "soccer"!

Today, teams wear matching shirts. This was not always so! The first matching shirts were worn in 1872. Before, teams wore matching caps! Today, players protect their shins. They keep them safe. They protect them with shin guards. Shin guards were invented in 1874.

A Game Played Around the World

After reading the story, answer the questions.
Fill in the circle next to the correct answer.

1. This story is mainly about

- ⓐ the game of soccer.
- ⓑ games around the world.
- ⓒ how soccer got its name.
- ⓓ what was used as a soccer ball.

2. When soccer is played around the world today, what makes it fair?

- ⓐ Players can trip each other.
- ⓑ Players cannot hold the ball.
- ⓒ The rules are the same for both teams.
- ⓓ The ball is not made of a pig's bladder.

3. Think about how the word *equal* relates to *same*. What words relate in the same way?

equal : same

- ⓐ met : led
- ⓑ team : players
- ⓒ matching : alike
- ⓓ long : shortened

4. In what year did the people meet in England to set the rules for soccer?

- ⓐ 1863
- ⓑ 1872
- ⓒ 1874
- ⓓ 2000

5. When you protect something, you

- ⓐ hold liquid.
- ⓑ keep it safe.
- ⓒ make it fair.
- ⓓ fill it with air.

Light and Dark

A penguin is a bird. A lapwing is a bird. A shark is a fish. The penguin, lapwing, and shark are the same in one way. How can birds be like a fish? How can a penguin, lapwing, and shark be the same in one way?

A penguin is two colors. It is black and white. The black is on the top. A penguin's back is black. It is dark above. The white is on the bottom. A penguin's belly is white. It is light below. Why is a penguin dark and light? A penguin's colors help keep it safe. Its colors help protect it.

Penguins swim a lot. Animals swimming below the penguin have a hard time seeing it. This is because the white color looks like the lighter top water. Animals swimming above the penguin have a hard time seeing it. This is because the black color looks like the dark deep water.

Lapwings are dark and light. They are dark green and white. The green is on the top. A lapwing's back is green. A lapwing's belly is white. Lapwings stand in green grass. They cannot be seen from above. They are green like the grass. When a lapwing flies, it is hidden from animals below. Its white belly is hard to see in the light sky. The lapwing's colors help protect it.

Sharks are dark and light, too. They are dark on top. They are light on the bottom. The dark and light coloring makes the shark hard to see. It helps disguise its shape. It helps hide its shape. A shark can sneak up on fish. It can sneak up on fish from above or below. Fish have a hard time seeing the shark in its light-and-dark disguise.

Light and Dark

After reading the story, answer the questions.
Fill in the circle next to the correct answer.

1. This story is mainly about

ⓐ light and dark.
ⓑ penguins and lapwings.
ⓒ the colors of some animals.
ⓓ how some animals sneak up on others.

2. How are the birds and the shark the same?

ⓐ They all are animals that are black.
ⓑ They are all dark above and light below.
ⓒ They all are animals that live in water.
ⓓ They are all light above and dark below.

3. Think about how the word **top** relates to **above**. Which words relate in the same way?

top : above

ⓐ dark : light
ⓑ color : black
ⓒ bottom : below
ⓓ penguin : bird

4. When something is disguised, it is

ⓐ safe.
ⓑ hidden.
ⓒ swimming.
ⓓ protected.

5. Why do lapwings need dark green backs?

ⓐ to sneak up on fish
ⓑ to fly in the light sky
ⓒ to swim in dark deep water
ⓓ to be hidden when they stand in dark green grass

Something Fast

"I do something fast," said Sam. "I do it faster than I can run. I do it faster than I can swim. I do it faster than I can ride my bike. I do it as fast as a car. I do it at 70 miles (110 kilometers) per hour. You do it, too." What can Sam do? What can you do, too?

Sam can sneeze. When you sneeze, air rushes down your nose. The air comes from your lungs. It rushes fast. It rushes faster than you can run. It rushes faster than you can swim. It rushes faster than you can ride a bike. It rushes as fast as a car. It rushes at 70 miles (110 kilometers) per hour.

Air is made out of gases. Tiny things are in air. The tiny things are too small to see. They float in the air. Some of the floating things are specks of dirt. Some of the floating things are germs. Germs are tiny forms of life. Germs can make you sick. When you breathe in, you take in air. You take in gas. You take in dirt and germs, too.

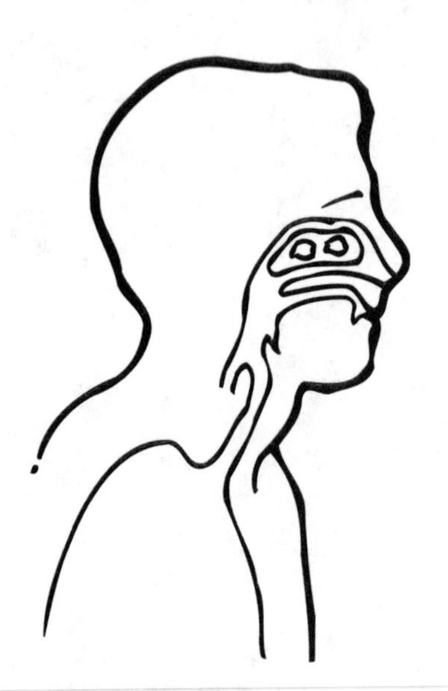

We have a trap in our nose. The trap protects the skin inside our nose. The trap is a layer of mucus. Mucus is like slime. It coats the inside of parts of our body. Our nose mucus traps dirt. It traps germs.

Sometimes a tiny speck irritates the inside of our nose. When something is irritated, it is bothered. The inside of our nose begins to itch. It begins to tingle. It makes us sneeze. The sneeze is a jet of air. It comes from our lungs. It goes down our nose. It sweeps mucus and irritating specks. It sweeps them out of our nose.

Something Fast

After reading the story, answer the questions.
Fill in the circle next to the correct answer.

1. What is the trap inside our nose made of?

ⓐ germs
ⓑ mucus
ⓒ lungs
ⓓ gases

2. What statement is true about when we sneeze?

ⓐ We sweep mucus into our nose.
ⓑ We sweep tiny germs into our nose.
ⓒ Air rushes from our nose down our lungs.
ⓓ Air rushes from our lungs down our nose.

3. This story is mainly about

ⓐ Sam.
ⓑ germs.
ⓒ sneezing.
ⓓ tiny specks.

4. Cats bother Sam. Cats make Sam sneeze. Sam is _____ by cats.

ⓐ rushed
ⓑ trapped
ⓒ protected
ⓓ irritated

5. Think about how the word **speck** relates to **tiny**. Which words relate in the same way?

speck : tiny

ⓐ dirt : air
ⓑ ride : bike
ⓒ germ : small
ⓓ lungs : nose

What the Red Flag Was For

A man was on a road. The man was jogging. He was holding a flag. The flag was red. The man was waving the red flag as he jogged on the road. The waving flag was a warning. What was it for?

Before cars, people used horses. Horse pulled carts. Horses pulled wagons. Horses pulled carriages. People rode on horses' backs. When cars were first made, they had to share the road with horses. A rule was made in England. The rule was about cars on roads. The rule was that a man had to jog in front of the car. The man had to wave a red flag. The flag warned people. It warned people that a car was coming.

In the United States, a man saw an accident. The accident was big. It was in a city. There was lots of traffic in the city. Many people were on the streets. Many horses were on the streets. Many cars were on the streets, too. The accident was where two streets crossed. It was where there was a lot of traffic. Cars, people, and horses were in the accident.

The man wanted to do something. He wanted to stop traffic accidents. What could he do? The man was Garrett Morgan. He was born in 1877. His mother had been a slave. Morgan thought. He thought and thought. Then, he thought of what to do. He could make something. He could make a traffic signal. It would have a red light. It would have a green light.

Morgan invented the traffic signal in 1923. His invention helped stop traffic accidents. Today, there are lots of cars. Today, horses do not share roads with cars. But we still use traffic signals. All of the traffic signals come from Morgan's invention.

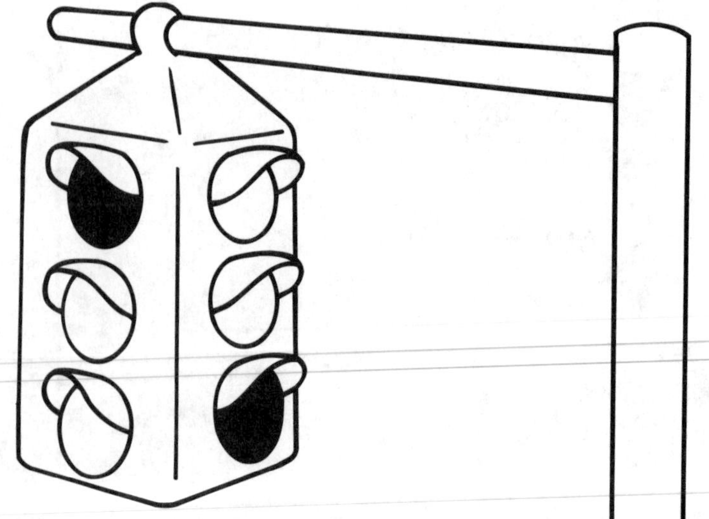

What the Red Flag Was For

After reading the story, answer the questions.
Fill in the circle next to the correct answer.

1. When did Morgan invent the traffic signal?

ⓐ 1776
ⓑ 1877
ⓒ 1923
ⓓ 2005

2. This story is mainly about

ⓐ cities with traffic.
ⓑ horses pulling wagons.
ⓒ England and the United States.
ⓓ cars on roads and traffic lights.

3. From the story, you can tell that long ago cars in England

ⓐ went slow on roads.
ⓑ did not go in cities.
ⓒ went faster than horses.
ⓓ did not share the road with horses.

4. If your school has a lot of traffic in the halls, it means that

ⓐ cars can go in the halls.
ⓑ your school is in the city.
ⓒ the halls have traffic lights.
ⓓ a lot of people go in the halls.

5. Think about how the word *red* relates to *stop*. What words relate in the same way?

red : stop

ⓐ green : go
ⓑ road : street
ⓒ flag : waving
ⓓ traffic : light

The Chinese New Year

Firecrackers pop! They explode! They go bang! They are set off on the Chinese New Year. They pop and explode on the Chinese New Year. They make a loud bang on the Chinese New Year. Why are firecrackers set off? Why are they part of the Chinese New Year? There is a story that tells why. The story is very old.

Long ago, there was a beast. The beast was bad. One winter, the beast went to a village. People were afraid. They were scared of the beast. They wanted the beast to go away. At the end of winter, they found out something. They found out by chance. They found out that the beast was afraid of something. The beast was scared of loud noises.

Bamboo is a kind of tree in China. Inside bamboo sticks, there are hollow spaces. Air is in the hollow spaces. People in the village burned bamboo sticks. The air in the hollow spaces heated up. Hot air takes up more space. It takes up more space than cold air. The hot air filled the hollow space. It pushed against the sticks. Pop! The sticks exploded with a loud noise. The loud noise scared the beast. The beast was afraid. It ran away.

Bamboo sticks were the first firecrackers. We do not use bamboo for firecrackers today. But firecrackers are like bamboo sticks. They are long. They are thin. They are like small bamboo sticks. They are part of the Chinese New Year.

The Chinese New Year happens every year. It begins on a full moon. It begins on the first full moon between January 20 and February 20. The holiday started a long time ago. It started over 4,000 years ago. The holiday marked the end of winter. It marked the start of spring.

The Chinese New Year

After reading the story, answer the questions.
Fill in the circle next to the correct answer.

1. This story is mainly about

- ⓐ how we make firecrackers.
- ⓑ beasts and a Chinese village.
- ⓒ the time of the Chinese New Year.
- ⓓ firecrackers and the Chinese New Year.

2. Why did the bamboo sticks explode when they were burned?

- ⓐ the sticks were thin
- ⓑ the air in the spaces heated up
- ⓒ the beast ran away from the loud noise
- ⓓ the people made them into the first firecrackers

3. Think about how the word *explode* relates to *pop*. What words relate in the same way?

- ⓐ end : start
- ⓑ beast : loud
- ⓒ scared : afraid
- ⓓ firecracker : tree

4. When you find out something by chance

- ⓐ you explode.
- ⓑ you are hollow.
- ⓒ you know you will scare a beast away.
- ⓓ you do not know you are going to find out.

5. What statement is true?

- ⓐ The Chinese New Year begins on a full moon.
- ⓑ The Chinese New Year marked the start of winter.
- ⓒ The Chinese New Year started over 5,000 years ago.
- ⓓ The Chinese New Year happens on the same day every year.

The Warmest Ocean

Which ocean is the warmest? Is it the Arctic? Is it the Atlantic? Is it the Indian? Is it the Pacific? It is not the Arctic. It is not the Atlantic. It is not the Pacific. The warmest ocean is the Indian.

The Persian Gulf is part of the Indian Ocean. The water in the Gulf is warm. It is warmest in the summer. The top water is the warmest. It can get to 100°F (38°C)! How hot is this? As hot as a hot tub!

The Red Sea is part of the Indian Ocean. The water in the Sea is warm. The top water is not the warmest. It is not hot where you swim. It is warmest deep down. It is hot at the bottom. This is because of volcanic activity. The volcanic activity is at the bottom of the Red Sea. It heats up the water. It can get to 133°F (56°C)! How hot is this? Hot enough to burn! Hot enough to burn off your skin!

The Indian Ocean is the third-largest ocean. It takes its name from India. It has the monsoon. The monsoon is a wind. It blows one way. This makes a dry time. Then it blows another way. This makes a rainy time.

A current is a flow. It is a one-way flow. The Indian Ocean has a current. It flows one way. The monsoon does something. It changes the current! The current flows the same way as the monsoon. Long ago, traders used the monsoon. They would sail away. They would go with the wind. They would trade far away. Then, they would sail back. They would sail back with the wind.

The Warmest Ocean

After reading the story, answer the questions.
Fill in the circle next to the correct answer.

1. What answer is *not* true?

ⓐ The Indian Ocean is the largest ocean.

ⓑ The Indian Ocean is the warmest ocean.

ⓒ The Persian Gulf is part of the Indian Ocean.

ⓓ Water at the bottom of the Red Sea is heated by volcanic activity.

2. What does the monsoon do to the current in the Indian Ocean?

ⓐ It heats it up.

ⓑ It makes a dry time.

ⓒ It changes the way it flows.

ⓓ It makes it the third-largest ocean.

3. This story is mainly about

ⓐ oceans.

ⓑ ocean currents.

ⓒ the warmest ocean.

ⓓ how the Indian Ocean got its name.

4. Why don't you get burned when you swim in the Red Sea?

ⓐ The water cannot burn your skin.

ⓑ You do not swim at the top of the sea.

ⓒ The water is not hot enough to burn you.

ⓓ You do not swim at the bottom of the sea.

5. Think about how the word *hot* relates to *cold.* What words relate in the same way?

hot : cold

ⓐ top : bottom

ⓑ current : flow

ⓒ Indian : ocean

ⓓ monsoon : wind

Raining Toads

One day it rained. It rained in France. It did not rain water. It rained toads! Toads fell from the sky. How could this be? How could toads fall from the sky? How could it rain toads in France?

Funnel clouds are columns of air. They are shaped like funnels. The air spins. The air spins fast. Funnel clouds twist down from thunderstorms. Sometimes they twist down to the ground. When a funnel cloud reaches the ground, it is called a tornado. Tornados are spinning winds.

Most tornados happen away from water. They happen inland. But some tornados happen over water. They form over rivers. They form over lakes. They form over oceans. Tornados that form over water are called waterspouts.

Tornados suck up warm air. Waterspouts suck up something else, too. They suck up water. They are columns of air and water. They spin fast. They can reach high into the sky. One waterspout was very big. It was over 1 mile (1.6 kilometers) high! Tornados pick up objects sometimes. The objects are picked up in the fast winds. Later, the objects are dropped.

Waterspouts pick up objects, too. Later, they are dropped. Fish have been picked up. Fish have been carried high in the air. They have been carried away from water. Then, they were dropped. When the fish were dropped, they fell from the sky. They landed on dry ground. They landed inland. Toads have been picked up, too. A lot of toads were picked up in France. They were carried high in the air. They were carried in the fast, spinning wind. Later, they were dropped. They fell from the sky. When they fell, it rained toads!

Raining Toads

After reading the story, answer the questions.
Fill in the circle next to the correct answer.

1. A funnel cloud becomes a tornado when it

ⓐ sucks up warm air.
ⓑ happens over water.
ⓒ twists down to the ground.
ⓓ picks up objects and drops them.

2. This story is mainly about

ⓐ tornados in France.
ⓑ toads and waterspouts.
ⓒ the day it rained toads.
ⓓ objects in funnel clouds.

3. Which statement is true?

ⓐ All waterspouts are tornados.
ⓑ All tornados are waterspouts.
ⓒ All funnel clouds become tornados.
ⓓ All toads are sucked up into waterspouts.

4. All waterspouts suck up

ⓐ toads and water.
ⓑ objects and toads.
ⓒ warm air and water.
ⓓ warm air and objects.

5. Think about how the word **carried** relates to **dropped**. Which words relate in the same way?

carried : dropped

ⓐ up : down
ⓑ rain : water
ⓒ spin : twist
ⓓ tornado : wind

A Very Cold Town

Verkhoyansk is a town. It is a cold town. It may be the coldest town in the world. It is in Russia. Russia is a big country. There are seven continents. Russia lies partly in two continents. It lies in Asia. It lies in Europe. Verkhoyansk lies in the part of Russia that is in East Asia.

When you open a door, cold air rushes in. In the cold town, the air outside is freezing. You do not want the cold air to rush in. The cold air will make the houses too cold. How do people keep their houses warm? What do they do when they have to come in? How do they stop the cold air from rushing in?

The people do not open just one door. They open three doors! They open the first door. They walk in. They shut it behind them. They open a second door. They go through it. They shut it behind them. Then, they open a third door. They walk through it. They shut it behind them. At last they are in the house!

How cold is the air people want to keep out? One time it was -90°F (-68°C)!!! There is moisture in your breath. In this town, sometimes the moisture in your breath freezes. It freezes and falls to the ground!

What about milk? The people in the cold town milk cows. The cows are milked inside warm sheds. The milk is poured into pots. Then, the pots are taken outside. The milk freezes in minutes! Then, the frozen milk is dumped out of the pots. The milk is in round, frozen chunks. The round, frozen chunks are stored in unheated sheds. When people want milk, they melt a chunk of milk.

A Very Cold Town

After reading the story, answer the questions.
Fill in the circle next to the correct answer.

1. How many doors do people walk through to get in and out of their houses in Verkhoyansk?

- ⓐ 1
- ⓑ 2
- ⓒ 3
- ⓓ 4

2. What can you tell about Asia from the story?

- ⓐ All of Asia is very cold.
- ⓑ All of Russia is very cold.
- ⓒ Parts of Asia are very cold.
- ⓓ Russia is the only country in Asia.

3. This story is mainly about

- ⓐ Russia
- ⓑ the continents
- ⓒ how to store milk
- ⓓ a town in East Asia

4. Why might people stay in Verkhoyansk?

- ⓐ There is no way to get out.
- ⓑ There are many things to mine, like gold and coal.
- ⓒ It is in the part of Russia that is in East Asia.
- ⓓ It gets so cold that the moisture in one's breath can freeze.

5. Think about how the word *hot* relates to *melt*. What words relate in the same way?

hot : melt

- ⓐ milk : chunk
- ⓑ cold : freeze
- ⓒ moisture : air
- ⓓ country : continent

Where Fish Can Swim in Trees

Fish live in water. Fish swim. But some fish swim among tree branches! They eat fruit. The fruit is high. It is high in the tree branches! How can this be? How can fish swim among high branches? How can fish eat fruit high in the tree? The fish are in South America. There are seven continents. South America is one of the continents.

A big river is in South America. It is the Amazon River. The Amazon River is long. Around the river is a forest. It is a rain forest. It is the Amazon rain forest. The Amazon rain forest is big. It is the biggest in the world.

The rain forest has seasons. It has a rainy season. It has a dry season. The rainy season is wet. It rains and rains. All the rain fills up the river. The water rises. The water spills over. It floods. The water rises up to the treetops. This is when fish can swim among tree branches. This is when fish can eat fruit from the tree!

South America has more than rain forests. It has grasslands. Cowboys work in the grasslands. The cowboys work hard. They herd cattle. The cattle eat grass. Some animals in the grasslands are wild. One wild animal is a bird. It is a rhea. A rhea is big. It is the biggest bird in North and South America. A rhea cannot fly. It runs. It runs fast across the grasslands.

A rhea uses its wings. A rhea cannot fly. How can it use its wings? A rhea uses its wings when it runs fast. It uses them as sails! The rhea raises one wing. It lowers the other wing. The wing sails help the rhea. They help the bird change directions.

Where Fish Can Swim in Trees

After reading the story, answer the questions.
Fill in the circle next to the correct answer.

1. This story is mainly about

ⓐ the continents.

ⓑ a South American river and a forest.

ⓒ South American grasslands and a bird.

ⓓ some South American animals and where they live.

2. Some fish can eat fruit in high tree branches

ⓐ when it rains.

ⓑ when it is the dry season.

ⓒ when it is in the grasslands.

ⓓ when the water floods and rises.

3. Think about how the word *dry* relates to *wet*. What words relate in the same way?

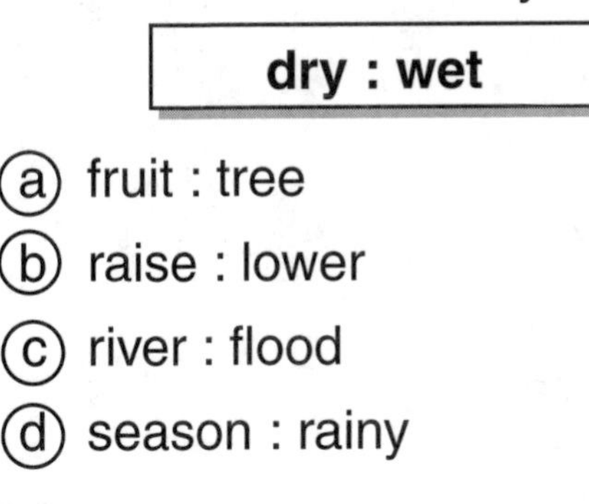

dry : wet

ⓐ fruit : tree

ⓑ raise : lower

ⓒ river : flood

ⓓ season : rainy

4. The rhea

ⓐ can fly.

ⓑ lives in the rain forest.

ⓒ can use its wings as sails.

ⓓ is the biggest bird in the world.

5. From the story, you can tell that South America is

ⓐ the biggest continent

ⓑ one of seven continents

ⓒ a continent with wild animals only

ⓓ the only continent with a rain forest

The Tale that Traveled

A tale is a story. Long ago, a tale was told. The story was told in West Africa. The tale was called "Talk! Talk!" The tale traveled. It traveled to the United States. How did the tale travel? How did it get to the United States?

People from Africa traveled to other places. Some were taken as slaves. They were taken from their homes. They were brought to new places. Some of the slaves were taken to the United States. The slaves told the tale. The tale traveled with slaves. There are no slaves in the United States today. Still, the tale is told. The tale goes like this:

A farmer was digging. He was digging yams. One yam said, "Ouch! You are hurting me!" The farmer jumped up. He was afraid. He ran down the road. He came to a fisherman. The fisherman had a net. He used the net to catch fish.

The farmer told the fisherman what the yam said. The fisherman did not believe the farmer. He knew yams could not say, "Ouch! You are hurting me!" Just then, the fisherman's net talked! What did the net say? It said, "Yams can't talk." The farmer and the fisherman were afraid. They ran down the road. They ran to the king.

The king was sitting on his royal stool. A stool is a chair without a back or arms. The farmer and the fisherman talked to the king. They told him a yam and a net had talked. The king was mad. He told the farmer and the fisherman to stop telling lies. The king told the men that lies were bad. Lies about talking yams and nets could make people afraid. And do you know what the king's royal stool said? "You are right!"

The Tail that Traveled

After reading the story, answer the questions.
Fill in the circle next to the correct answer.

1. This story is mainly about

ⓐ a talking yam.
ⓑ a tale that traveled.
ⓒ a king's royal stool.
ⓓ a farmer and a fisherman.

2. Where was the tale "Talk! Talk!" told first?

ⓐ West Africa
ⓑ East Africa
ⓒ South Africa
ⓓ North Africa

3. What answer is in the right order for how things talked?

ⓐ yam, stool, net
ⓑ net, yam, stool
ⓒ yam, net, stool
ⓓ stool, net, yam

4. Think about how the word *tale* relates to *story*. What words relate in the same way?

tale : story

ⓐ stool : chair
ⓑ afraid : talk
ⓒ fisherman : net
ⓓ traveled : United States

5. From the story, you can tell that

ⓐ tales stay in one place.
ⓑ some tales are told many times.
ⓒ stools can talk, but yams can't.
ⓓ "Talk! Talk!" is a tale only told to kings.

Paper

You are reading words. What are the words on? The words are on paper. Books are made of paper. Newspapers are paper. You can write and draw on paper. You can wrap things and make kites with paper. You use paper a lot. You use it every day!

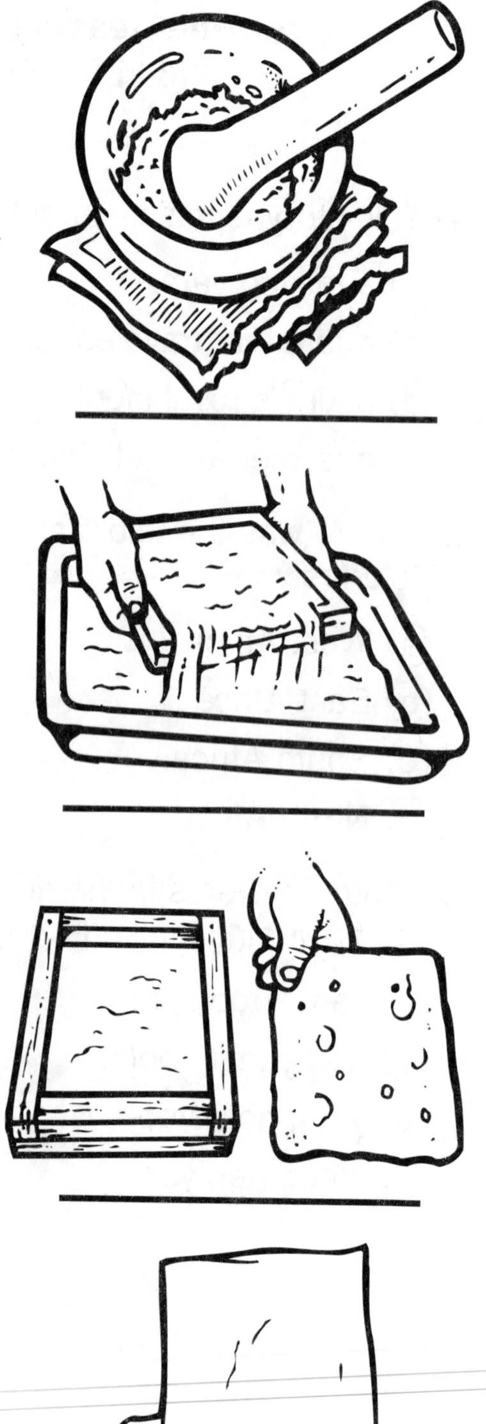

Long ago, people did not have paper. They made clay tablets. They scratched letters in the tablets. The tablets were big. They were heavy. They took a long time to make. Around 3000 B.C., people in Egypt made something new. They made a type of paper. It was made of reeds. Reeds are a kind of plant. It was better than tablets. Still, it took a long time to make.

The first true paper was made in China. It was made in the year 105. A man mixed things. He mixed tree bark, fishnets, and bamboo. He put them in a pot. He added water. He hit the mixture. He hit it with a stick. The stick was big and heavy. The man hit the mixture again and again. The mixture turned into mush. The man took the mush. He spread it over a screen. He let it dry. He had made the first true paper!

No one else knew how to make paper. Then, in the year 751, some men were captured. The men were from China. They knew how to make paper. The men were brought to a new city. The captured men taught other people how to make paper. Soon, people all over the world learned how to make paper.

What did paper do for science? Paper did a lot for science. Paper is light. It is easy to move. People could write down what they knew on paper. They could share what they knew with people far away.

Paper

After reading the story, answer the questions.
Fill in the circle next to the correct answer.

1. What did people use in Egypt to make paper?

ⓐ clay
ⓑ reeds
ⓒ bamboo
ⓓ fishnets

2. This story is mainly about

ⓐ China.
ⓑ paper.
ⓒ tablets.
ⓓ science.

3. Why is paper better than tablets?

ⓐ Paper is a mixture.
ⓑ Paper has words on it.
ⓒ Paper is light and easy to move.
ⓓ Paper is made all over the world.

4. Which answer is in the correct order? The first true paper was made by

ⓐ letting the mush dry, putting things in a pot, hitting the mixture.
ⓑ hitting the mixture, putting things in a pot, spreading mush over a screen.
ⓒ putting things in a pot, letting the mush dry, spreading mush over a screen.
ⓓ putting things in a pot, hitting the mixture, spreading mush over a screen.

5. Think about how the word **light** relates to **heavy**. Which words relate in the same way?

light : heavy

ⓐ easy : hard
ⓑ spread : dry
ⓒ tablets : clay
ⓓ captured : knew

Race to the Pole

Antarctica is a continent. There are seven continents. Antarctica is the coldest. It is the windiest. It is the driest. Inland, it is a desert. The air is too cold to hold moisture. Ice covers the continent. Only a small bit of land is free of ice.

The South Pole lies in Antarctica. There was a race. It was a race to the Pole. No one had been to the South Pole. Who would be first? Who could battle the cold? Who could battle the wind? Who could battle the desert of ice?

The year was 1911. Two teams set off. One leader was Roald Amundsen. He was from Norway. He had eight men and 118 sled dogs. He and his men were good skiers. They knew how to work sled dogs. One leader was Robert Scott. He was from England. He had 32 men and 33 sled dogs. He had 17 ponies. He had two tractor sleds. The tractor sleds had motors.

Amundsen's team went fast. Some men skied. Some men drove the dog sleds. They got to the South Pole first. They put up a tent. They left a message. The message was for Scott. Scott's team did not go fast. The tractor sleds broke down. The motors got too cold. It was too cold for the ponies, too. Some men went back to the main camp. Scott and four men went on to the Pole. They did not take dogs. They pulled their own sled.

Scott's team got to the Pole. They took pictures. Scott wrote in his diary. Sadly, the team did not make it back. They ran out of food. It was too cold. It was too hard to pull the sled. Scott's pictures and diary were found. They helped us learn about the brave men.

Race to the Pole

After reading the story, answer the questions.
Fill in the circle next to the correct answer.

1. What did Roald Amundsen have more of?

ⓐ dogs
ⓑ sleds
ⓒ ponies
ⓓ tractors

2. This story is mainly about

ⓐ the South Pole.
ⓑ the continents.
ⓒ a race to the Pole.
ⓓ the man who was first to the Pole.

3. What is not true about Antarctica?

ⓐ It is the driest continent.
ⓑ It is the coldest continent.
ⓒ It is the biggest continent.
ⓓ It is the windiest continent.

4. What might have helped Robert Scott get back to camp?

ⓐ tractor sleds
ⓑ dogs to pull his sled
ⓒ ponies to pull his sled
ⓓ fewer men to pull his sled

5. Think about how the word *sled* relates to *snow*. What words relate in the same way?

sled : snow

ⓐ bike : ice
ⓑ plane : fly
ⓒ car : house
ⓓ boat : water

Firewood for Pay

Abby went to school long ago. She went in the 1600s. What was it like for Abby? Was it the same as today? No, it was not. In the 1600s, many children went to dame schools. Dame school teachers were women. The women would teach the school in their homes. Often, the school was in their kitchen. This way, the teacher could cook. She could do her housework while the children worked.

How did the children pay the teacher? They brought firewood! The teacher would use the firewood. She would use it to cook. She would use it to heat her house. What if children forgot to bring firewood? They could not sit by the fire. They had to sit away from the heat.

How old was Abby? Abby was six. She would go to school for two years. She would go until she was eight. Most dame schools students were six to eight years old. There were more boys than girls. The schools started in the early morning. They started at seven A.M. They ended in the late afternoon. They ended at four or five P.M.

Abby's school did not have a blackboard. It did not have chalk. It did not have books. It did not have paper. It did not have pencils. How did Abby learn to read? She had a hornbook. A hornbook was flat. It was wood. It was a flat, wooden board. The wooden board had a handle.

hornbook

Numbers were carved on one side. The alphabet was carved on it, too. A piece of paper was on the other side. The alphabet was on the paper. A prayer was, too. How was the paper protected? It was protected with a thin sheet of animal horn. The thin sheet of animal horn protected the paper.

Firewood for Pay

After reading the story, answer the questions.
Fill in the circle next to the correct answer.

1. This story is mainly about

ⓐ school in the 1500s.
ⓑ school in the 1600s.
ⓒ school in the 1700s.
ⓓ school in the 1800s.

2. What time did dame schools start?

ⓐ four A.M.
ⓑ four P.M.
ⓒ seven A.M.
ⓓ seven P.M.

3. Why were dame schools often in the teacher's kitchen?

ⓐ so the teacher could write on the chalkboard
ⓑ so the teacher could put firewood on the fire
ⓒ so the teacher could cook while the children worked
ⓓ so the teacher could have a school not the same as today

4. Think about how the word *pencil* relates to *paper.* What words relate in the same way?

pencil : paper

ⓐ start : end
ⓑ book : read
ⓒ pay : teacher
ⓓ chalk : chalkboard

5. What is *not* true about the hornbook?

ⓐ It was a book.
ⓑ It had a paper on it.
ⓒ It had numbers carved in it.
ⓓ It had a sheet of animal horn.

Why Pant?

Think about running. You can run fast. You can run fast when you play games. You can run fast in a race. What happens when you run fast? What happens when you play running games? What happens when you run a fast race? You begin to pant. You begin to gasp. You breathe with quick, deep breaths.

Why do you pant? Why do you gasp? Why do you breathe with quick, deep breaths? You pant when you need something. What do you need? You need oxygen. Oxygen is a gas. It is a gas in our air. We take in oxygen when we breathe.

We breathe faster when we pant. We take in more air with each breath, too. We take in more oxygen. We get more oxygen faster. We get the oxygen we need. When we get enough oxygen, we stop panting. We breathe slower. We do not gasp for air.

Why do we need more oxygen? Why do we need to pant so that we take in more air? Running is work. Running is a kind of exercise. Exercise is work. Our muscles work when we exercise. They work making our bones move. It takes energy to work. It takes energy to run. It takes energy to exercise. Our muscles need energy. How do they get it?

Our muscles get energy from sugar. The sugar is special. It is a special kind. It is called glucose. We get glucose from food. Our muscles need something to use glucose. They need oxygen. Glucose cannot be used for energy unless there is oxygen. Panting gets us more oxygen. Panting makes it so we can use more glucose. Panting makes it so we get more energy.

Why Pant?

After reading the story, answer the questions.
Fill in the circle next to the correct answer.z

1. When you pant

ⓐ you breathe slower and take in less air.

ⓑ you breathe faster and take in less air.

ⓒ you breathe slower and take in more air.

ⓓ you breathe faster and take in more air.

2. Where do we get glucose?

ⓐ from food

ⓑ from oxygen

ⓒ from energy

ⓓ from exercise

3. This story is mainly about

ⓐ why we pant.

ⓑ why we exercise.

ⓒ why oxygen is a gas.

ⓓ why glucose is special.

4. What might take the most energy?

ⓐ sitting

ⓑ reading

ⓒ jumping

ⓓ sleeping

5. Think about how the word **slow** relates to **fast**. Which words relate in the same way?

slow : fast

ⓐ pant : gasp

ⓑ begin : stop

ⓒ breathe : air

ⓓ sugar : glucose

Answer Key

Page 3
1. c
2. a
3. d
4. a

Page 4
1. c
2. d
3. a
4. d

Page 5
1. b
2. c
3. a
4. c

Page 6
1. d
2. d
3. b
4. a

Page 7
1. a
2. d
3. b
4. c

Page 8
1. b
2. c
3. d
4. a

Page 9
1. d
2. a
3. b
4. c

Page 11
1. b
2. b
3. a
4. d
5. c

Page 13
1. d
2. c
3. d
4. a
5. b

Page 15
1. d
2. c
3. a
4. d
5. c

Page 17
1. c
2. a
3. d
4. a
5. b

Page 19
1. d
2. b
3. d
4. c
5. c

Page 21
1. a
2. c
3. c
4. a
5. b

Page 23
1. c
2. b
3. c
4. b
5. d

Page 25
1. b
2. d
3. c
4. d
5. c

Page 27
1. c
2. d
3. a
4. d
5. a

Page 29
1. d
2. b
3. c
4. d
5. a

Page 31
1. a
2. c
3. c
4. d
5. a

Page 33
1. c
2. b
3. a
4. c
5. a

Page 35
1. c
2. c
3. d
4. b
5. b

Page 37
1. d
2. d
3. b
4. c
5. b

Page 39
1. b
2. a
3. c
4. a
5. b

Page 41
1. b
2. b
3. c
4. d
5. a

Page 43
1. a
2. c
3. c
4. b
5. d

Page 45
1. b
2. c
3. c
4. d
5. a

Page 47
1. d
2. a
3. a
4. c
5. b